PIZZA WITCH

♡ Sarah Graley

SHINY SWORD PRESS

ISBN: 9780993384349

PIZZA WITCH DELUXE EDITION

COPYRIGHT 2017 SARAH GRALEY
ALL RIGHTS RESERVED

PUBLISHED BY SHINY SWORD PRESS,
BIRMINGHAM, UK

PIZZA WITCH

BY SARAH GRALEY

LETTERING BY STEF PURENINS

...YOU DELIVER WITHIN HALF AN HOUR OR IT'S FREE, RIGHT?

UH...YES?

OK, BYE!

SO WE'RE DOING THIS?

YEAH!!

...WITHIN 30 MINUTES?

UHHH...

WELL, WE'VE MADE A COMMITMENT NOW...

...SO LET'S RIDE.

EH?

AH.

USE YOUR SPELLS!!

GNRHH!

I ONLY KNOW PIZZA SPELLS!

USE YOUR PIZZA SPELLS!!

OK!

I'LL SPAWN SOME PIZZAS THAT I MADE EARLIER!!

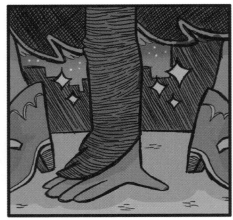

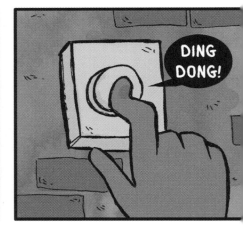

PIZZA WITCH GETS HER FIRST BAD REVIEW

PARK MY BROOM?

YOU KNOW I GOT YOU.

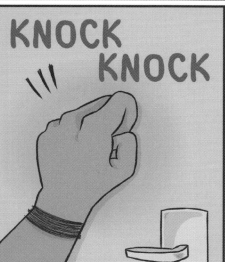

KNOCK
KNOCK

ONE LARGE PEPPERONI, FOR A MISTER –

PIZZA WITCH, I NEED YOUR HELP!

EEP!

IT'S AN EMERGENCY THAT ONLY **YOU** CAN SOLVE!

COME QUICK, WE'RE NEARLY **OUT OF TIME!**

WHOA, SLOW DOWN DUDE!

PIZZA WITCH, I ORDERED A PIZZA TO SUMMON YOU HERE TODAY...

...BECAUSE I'M IN **DIRE NEED** OF YOUR **POWERFUL WITCH MAGIC!** I FEEL LIKE IT'S THE ONLY THING THAT WILL SAVE ME NOW!

I NEED YOU! I NEED YOU...

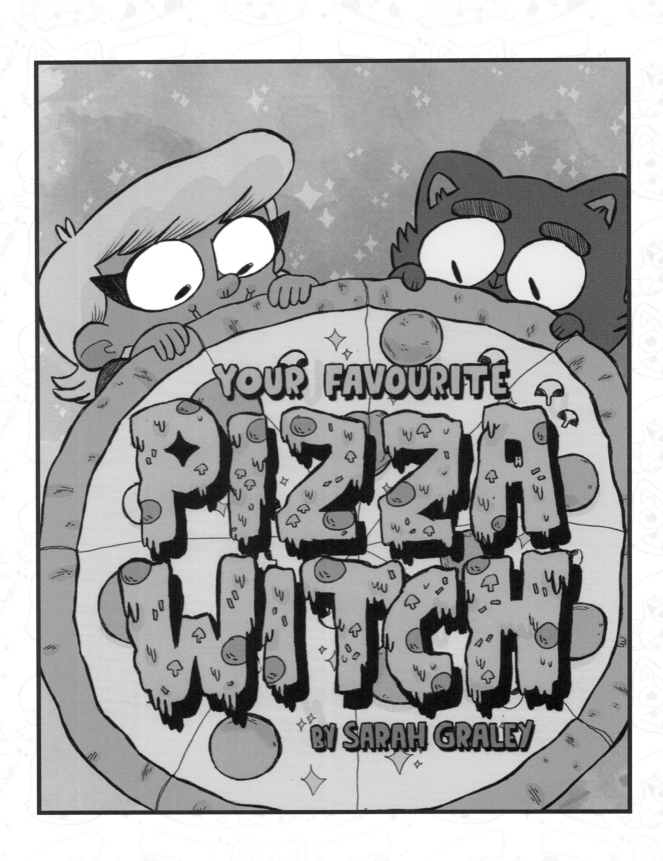

THIS WAS THE FRONT COVER TO THE FIRST EDITION OF PIZZA WITCH - ORIGINALLY TITLED "YOUR FAVOURITE PIZZA WITCH", AFTER THE NAME OF ROXY & GEORGE'S PIZZA DELIVERY COMPANY.

THE FIRST EDITION OF PIZZA WITCH WAS LIMITED TO 800 COPIES, AND WAS PRINTED AS PART OF MY KICKSTARTER FOR OUR SUPER ADVENTURE - EVERYONE WHO BACKED £20 OR MORE GOT A COPY WHEN WE HIT ONE OF THE STRETCH GOALS.

THE KICKSTARTER DID REALLY WELL (IT'S THE 9TH MOST FUNDED UK COMICS KICKSTARTER AT THE TIME OF WRITING THIS) SO IT WAS NICE TO BE ABLE TO GIVE BACKERS SOMETHING EXTRA AS MY WAY OF SAYING THANKS!

PIZZA WITCH PROCESS

STEP 1 - THUMBNAILS

WHEN WRITING MY SCRIPTS I LIKE TO STORYBOARD THEM AT THE SAME TIME. STORYBOARDS CAN BE REALLY ROUGH - AS LONG AS I CAN FIGURE OUT WHAT THEY MEAN LATER ON!

SOMETIMES I'LL DO SEVERAL DRAFTS OF THE SAME PAGE BUT GETTING IT DOWN QUICKLY HELPS TO CAPTURE THE INITIAL IDEAS THAT I HAVE FOR THE PAGE.

I USUALLY DO MY THUMBNAILS ON RANDOM BITS OF PAPER, OR IF I'M NOT BEING AN IDIOT, IN A NICE SKETCHBOOK SO THAT IT'S ALL SAFE IN ONE PLACE.

PIZZA WITCH WAS THUMBNAILED ON RANDOM BITS OF PAPER.

STEP 2 - DRAWING

BEFORE SWITCHING TO DIGITAL, I USED TO SKETCH COMIC PAGES IN PENCIL BEFORE INKING THEM WITH BIRO.

I WOULD THEN SCAN THE FINISHED BIRO DRAWING INTO PHOTOSHOP WHERE I WOULD THEN DO A LOT OF CLEAN-UP.

ALTHOUGH I LIKE THE SCRAPPY LINES THAT INKING WITH BIRO BRINGS, I'M QUITE HAPPY WITH MY MOVE TO INKING COMICS DIGITALLY.

STEP 3 - COLOUR

I ALWAYS COLOUR USING PHOTOSHOP. FOR PIZZA WITCH I DISCOVERED THE OVERLAY LAYER SETTING WHICH I USED A LOT FOR PIZZA SMELL VISUALISATIONS AND SPARKLES.

I USED BLOCK COLOUR FOR THE CHARACTERS BUT I USED WATERCOLOUR EFFECT BRUSHES TO ADD TEXTURE TO THE BACKGROUNDS AND ENVIRONMENTS.

PIZZA WITCH WAS THE PROJECT WHERE I STARTED TO GET MORE CONFIDENT WITH COLOURING STYLES AND I WAS HAPPY WITH THE LOOK OF THE FINISHED COMIC.

STEP 4 - LETTERING

HI! THIS IS STEF BRIEFLY TAKING OVER!

FOR THIS NEW VERSION OF PIZZA WITCH I TRIED TO FIND A FONT THAT WOULD SUIT SARAH'S STYLE AND SETTLED ON THIS ONE.

THE SPEECH BUBBLES IN THE ORIGINAL VERSION WERE PART OF THE ORIGINAL BIRO-DRAWN LINEWORK SO IT WAS A BIT TRICKY IN PLACES EDITING AND PLACING NEW SPEECH BUBBLES THAT WOULDN'T LOOK TOO WEIRD OR OUT OF PLACE.

I ADDED SOME EXTRA "MAGIC" TO THE BITS WHERE ROXY IS CASTING PIZZA SPELLS AT THE START FOR FUN. IT GIVES IT SOME REAL GRAVITAS AND SPOOOOOOKINESS.

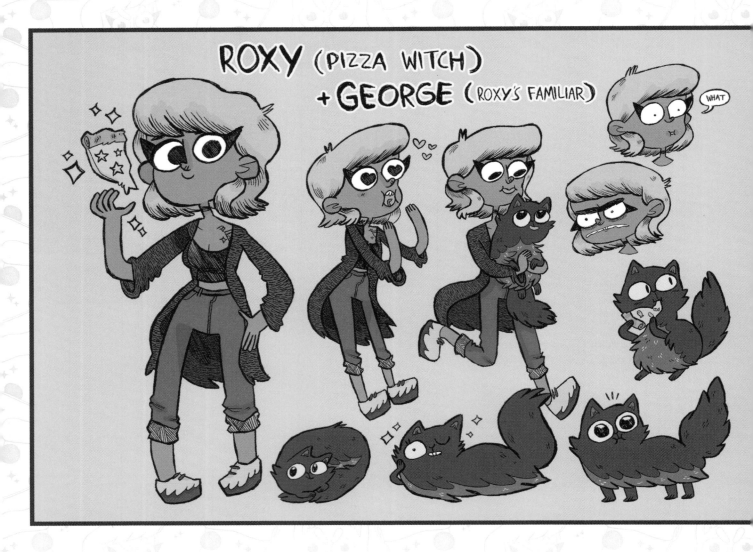

ROXY (PIZZA WITCH)
+ GEORGE (ROXY'S FAMILIAR)

WHAT

TOBY
OUR MOON & STARS

ROXY

WANTED ROXY TO HAVE A MODERN DAY WITCHY VIBE SO I REPLACED THE STEREOTYPICAL BLACK CLOAK WITH A LONG, FLOWING CARDIGAN, AND REPLACED THE POINTY HAT WITH A BASEBALL CAP UNIFORM FOR HER PIZZA BUSINESS!

ALSO WANTED HER SHOES TO LOOK LIKE THEY HAD CHEESE MELTING ON THE TOP.

YOU KNOW.

LIKE A PIZZA.

GEORGE

GEORGE IS TOTALLY BASED ON OUR OWN WITCHY BLACK CAT, TOBY. (BUT WITH BIGGER EYEBROWS)

I GAVE HIM AN ELECTRIC BLUE TUMMY SO THAT YOU KNOW THAT HE WAS A VERY STYLISH PERSON BEFORE HE TURNED INTO A CAT. ALSO, ELECTRIC BLUE IS PRETTY CUTE.

EVELYN

EVELYN IS JUST A MIX OF COOL FASHION THINGS THAT I WISH THAT I COULD PULL OFF.

I DREW THIS MOON BAG BEFORE I ACTUALLY OWNED THIS ACTUAL MOON BAG. IT'S NOW SADLY REALLY SCUFFED UP, BUT THAT DOESN'T STOP THIS FACT FROM BEING KIND OF FUN.

EVELYN (ROXY'S LOVE INTEREST)

DREAMIEST BABE

HERE'S A COLLECTION OF PANELS IN THEIR LINEWORK PHASE, BEFORE THE IMAGES WERE CLEANED UP, AND THE MAGIC OF COLOUR HAD BEEN APPLIED IN PHOTOSHOP.

ALSO, THIS IS WHAT THE ORIGINAL SPEECH BUBBLES LOOKED LIKE TOO!

PG5

PG6

PG7

PG8

SARAH GRALEY IS A UK-BASED COMIC ARTIST AND WRITER. SHE WROTE AND DREW THIS BOOK! ALONG WITH OTHER TITLES SUCH AS 'LIL' POOPY SUPERSTAR' (A RICK AND MORTY MINISERIES) AND 'KIM REAPER' PUBLISHED BY ONI PRESS. SHE ALSO MAKES AN AUTOBIOGRAPHICAL COMIC TITLED 'OUR SUPER ADVENTURE' ABOUT HER, HER PARTNER STEF, AND THEIR FOUR CATS.

YOU CAN FIND OUT MORE ABOUT HER AT **SARAHGRALEY.COM**

STEF PURENINS IS A MUSICIAN WHO DOES SOME COMIC LETTERING AND DESIGNS BITS AND PIECES. HE LETTERED THIS BOOK, AND ARRANGED THE BONUS CONTENT BIT TOO. HE MAKES VIDEO GAME SONGS AS 'TINY SPELLS', BLEEPY POP WITH SARAH AS 'SONIC THE COMIC' AND SHOUTY INDIE POP WITH 'MAYBE DON'T'.

FIND OUT MORE ABOUT HIM IN **OUR SUPER ADVENTURE!**

ALSO BY SARAH GRALEY

OUR SUPER ADVENTURE

A COLLECTION OF 200 DIARY COMICS ABOUT BEING SOPPY, EATING TOO MUCH PIZZA AND LIVING WITH FOUR CATS AND ONE CAT-LIKE BOY.

OUR SUPER ADVENTURE HAS BEEN A WEBCOMIC SINCE 2012 AT OURSUPERADVENTURE.COM AND THIS BOOK WAS FUNDED THROUGH AN INCREDIBLE KICKSTARTER CAMPAIGN WITH EVEN MORE INCREDIBLE BACKERS!

AVAILABLE NOW FROM SARAHGRALEY.COM!

OTHER NOTABLE TITLES

RICK AND MORTY - LIL' POOPY SUPERSTAR (ONI PRESS)

MR. POOPYBUTTHOLE IS IN TROUBLE, AND HE TURNS TO THE ONE PERSON HE CAN TRUST: SUMMER SMITH! SHE'S MORE THAN WILLING TO HELP, BUT IS HE TELLING HER THE WHOLE TRUTH? WRITTEN AND ILLUSTRATED BY SARAH GRALEY (OUR SUPER ADVENTURE) AND COLORED BY MILDRED LOUIS (AGENTS OF THE REALM), SUMMER AND MR. POOPYBUTTHOLE EMBARK ON THEIR VERY OWN FANTASTIC ADVENTURE ACROSS SPACE, COMPLETE WITH JAILBREAKS, HIJACKINGS, AND HIGH SCHOOL PROM. PLUS! BACKUP COMICS FEATURING GOOD OL' RICK AND MORTY, ILLUSTRATED BY MARC ELLERBY.

KIM REAPER (ONI PRESS)

LIKE MOST UNIVERSITY STUDENTS, KIM WORKS A PART-TIME JOB TO MAKE ENDS MEET. UNLIKE MOST UNIVERSITY STUDENTS, KIM'S JOB IS PRETTY DANG COOL: SHE'S A GRIM REAPER, TASKED WITH GUIDING SOULS INTO THE AFTERLIFE.

LIKE MOST UNIVERSITY STUDENTS, BECKA HAS A SUPER INTENSE UNREQUITED CRUSH. UNLIKE MOST UNIVERSITY STUDENTS, BECKA'S CRUSH IS ON A BEAUTIFUL GOTHIC ANGEL THAT FREQUENTS THE UNDERWORLD. OF COURSE, SHE DOESN'T KNOW THAT...YET.

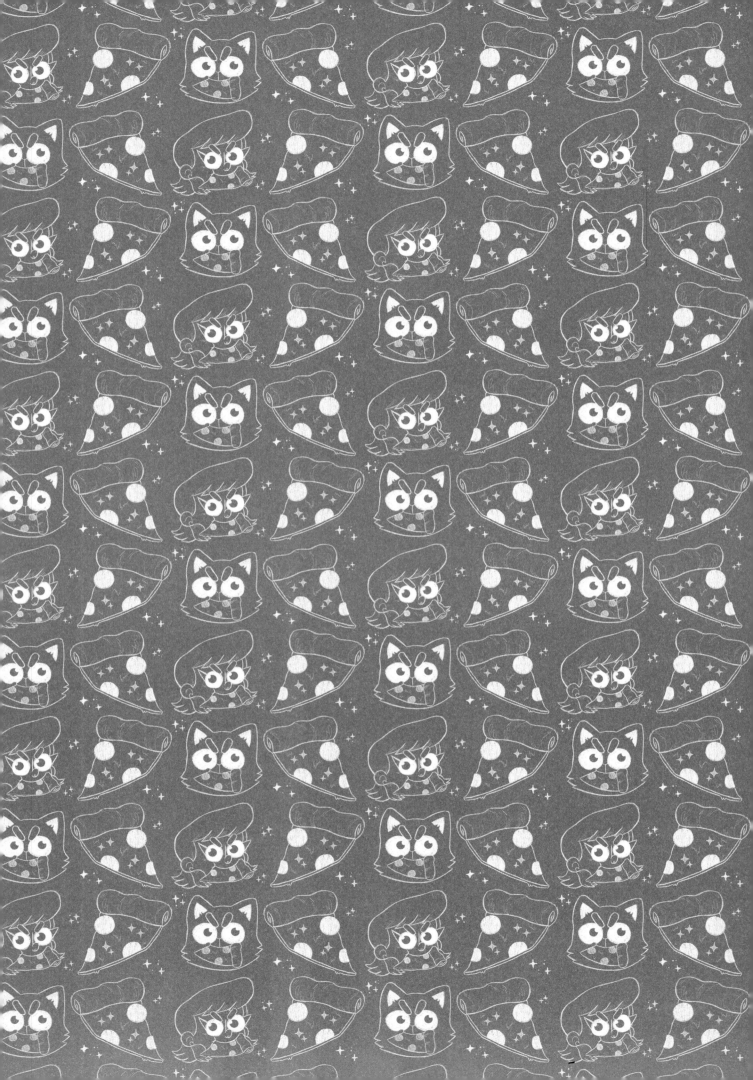